Handling
Your Money

Also available in the "How To Series"

Praying The Lord's Prayer	Terry Virgo
Effective Evangelism	Ben Davies
Growing Up As A Christian	Roger Day

For further information on the "How To Series" and New Frontiers, please write to New Frontiers 21-23 Clarendon Villas, Hove, Brighton, East Sussex, BN3 3RE.

SERIES EDITOR
TERRY VIRGO

How to...
STUDY SERIES

HANDLING
YOUR MONEY

JOHN HOUGHTON

NEW FRONTIERS

WORD PUBLISHING

Word (UK) Ltd
Milton Keynes, England

WORD BOOKS AUSTRALIA
Heathmont, Victoria, Australia
SUNDAY SCHOOL CENTRE WHOLESALE
Salt River, South Africa
ALBY COMMERCIAL ENTERPRISES PTE LTD
Scotts Road, Singapore
CONCORDE DISTRIBUTORS LTD
Havelock North, New Zealand
CROSS (HK) CO
Hong Kong
PRAISE INC
Quezon City, Philippines

HANDLING YOUR MONEY
© John Houghton 1986
First published by Coastlands July 1986
Revised edition 1987, Word (UK) Ltd/New Frontiers

ISBN 0-85009-176-4 (Australia 1-86258-023-5)

Printed and bound in Great Britain by Cox & Wyman Ltd, Reading.

Introduction

The 'How to' series has been published with a definite purpose in view. It provides a set of work books suitable either for house groups or individuals who want to study a particular Bible theme in a practical way. The goal is not simply to look up verses and fill in blank spaces on the page, but to fill in gaps in our lives and so increase our fruitfulness and our knowledge of God.

Peter wrote his letters to 'stimulate wholesome thinking' (2 Peter 3:1). He required his readers to think as well as read! We hope the training manual approach of this book will have the same effect. *Stop, think, apply* and *act* are key words.

If you are using the book on your own, we suggest you work through the chapters systematically, Bible at your side and pen in hand. If you are doing it as a group activity, it is probably best to do all the initial reading and task work before the group sessions — this gives more time for discussion on key issues which may be raised.

All quotations from the Bible are from the New International Version, which the reader is expected to use in filling in the study material.

Terry Virgo
Series Editor

NEW FRONTIERS is a team ministry led by Terry Virgo and involved in planting and equipping churches according to New Testament principles with a view to reaching this generation with the gospel of the Kingdom. They are also responsible for a wide range of conferences, training programmes and the production of printed and audio teaching materials.

Contents

Before you Begin . . .

People die of famine because nations don't handle their money properly. Thousands go to court each year because they fall into unpayable debt. Millions struggle to make ends meet. You may be one of them.

Or you might be quite comfortably off. No great financial worries, a reasonable amount of giving, nice home and holidays in the sun.

But, whether struggling or succeeding, you need to face this question: Are you handling your money according to God's Word?

Does the Bible actually say much about money? Yes, it does. An enormous amount, in fact. It has been estimated that one in every sixteen verses in the New Testament has to do with wealth and poverty. How we manage our money is without doubt a spiritual issue.

This study book is intended to teach the basic biblical principles of 'home economics' — personal financial management. However, it is not a book of economic theories. Everything God says to us has practical implications. Truth is meant to change our behaviour. So, each chapter concludes with a list of 'things to do' and space to write in the date when you begin to do them.

Part One GIVERS AND GETTERS

Lesson 1 GOD THE GIVER

If we're going to arrive at a correct understanding of what the Bible teaches about money and possessions we must begin with God Himself. What is He like? What does He think about the material world? How does He view our attitudes? Is He doing anything about it? To answer this we must return to

As it was in the beginning
God is a triune God; that means He is three-in-one — Father, Son and Holy Spirit. Christians sometimes express this when they repeat 2 Cor 13:14 as a grace at the end of a meeting.

God is also Love (1 Jn 4:8). Throughout all eternity the three Persons of the Godhead have been bathed in a fellowship of love. We catch a glimpse of this in Jesus' prayer in Jn 17:24. From when was Jesus loved?

From ....

This doesn't mean, however, that God is a mutual self-admiration society! His love is of a very special kind: it's a sacrificial, self-giving love.

Although we find it hard to understand what that means in eternity, we do know that one of the fruits of God's sacrificial love was the creation of the Universe, and in particular, our planet Earth.

9

The pinnacle of this creation is mankind. What does Psa 8:5 say we are crowned with?

....

Man was made in the image of God (Gen 1:26-27) to reflect His glory and to receive His love.

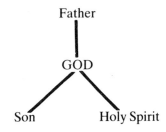

Father

GOD

Son   Holy Spirit

gave in love

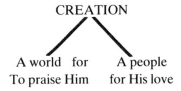

CREATION

A world   for   A people
To praise Him   for His love

Look up these references about God's original creation and underline the appropriate word in the question.

Was the world made good/bad/indifferent? Gen 1:4, 31.

Was it a world of scarcity/plenty/enough? Gen 1:11, 20-22.

Did God ignore/curse/bless mankind? Gen 1:28; 2:18, 20-22.

Did He intend mankind to be rich/poor/just coping? Gen 1:29; 2:9, 16.

The Fall

As we know from Genesis 3, all did not go well. The serpent seduced Eve into disobeying God. Adam joined her in the sin. Together they plunged themselves and the world into ruin.

Many griefs flowed from the Fall. We must take note of two at this point.

1. Sin resulted in the creation of want.

Under the judgement of God the earth became reluctant to yield its blessings — Gen 3:17-19.

It became a place of disasters — Gen 12:10; Lk 21:10-11.

It was made subject to futility, or meaninglessness — Eccl 1:2-11; Rom 8:20.

2. Mankind became covetous.

Something had changed in the human heart. Instead of delighting in God and enjoying His provision with thanksgiving, the desire to possess took over. Adam and Eve began to lust after, or to covet, things as an end in themselves.

What started then became characteristic of society without God i.e. the world. We can see this if we compare how Eve viewed the forbidden fruit with the way John describes his contemporary world.

Gen 3:6	1 Jn 2:16 RSV
When the woman saw	For all that is
that the tree was	in the world
good for food	the lust of the flesh
and	and
pleasing to the eye,	the lust of the eyes
and also	and
desirable for gaining wisdom,	the pride of life
she took	is not of the Father

Fallen man has become greedy — Eph 4:19; 1 Tim 6:9-10
                covetous — Psa 10:3
                thieving — Micah 2:2
                unequal — Prov 10:15
                unjust — Amos 5:11-12; 8:4-6.
How very different from the heart of God!

Providence and redemption
But God has not abandoned his world. Look up Psa 24:1. Write down what belongs to the Lord.

....

....

Because it's still His, He continues to care for this planet and for those who live upon it. We call this God's providence. There are four things to know about it:
1. God created the world — Gen 1:1; Rev 4:11; Heb 11:3.
2. God sustains the world — Heb 1:3; Acts 17:24-28.
3. God owns all things — Deut 10:14; Psa 50:10-12; 1 Chron 29:10-16.

4. God provides generously — Psa 74:16-17; Gen 8:22; Psa 145:15-16; 147:8-9; Acts 14:16-17.

Providence shows us that God is very much concerned about our material needs.

But our greatest need is for a spiritual redemption. That must precede our material redemption. Both come from God's heart of 'giving-love'.

Gen 12:2-3 is a very important promise. Write it out.

....

....

....

God's redemption focuses on the gift of His Son — Jn 3:16. By His death, Jesus brought to fulfilment the ancient promise given to Abraham. Read Gal 3:14.

What was that promise? ....

Who is it for? ....

What is immediately apparent after the outpouring of the Spirit (see Acts 2) is the fact that the early believers saw that the fulfilment of that promise had social as well as spiritual implications for them. A new community lifestyle quickly came into being. One of the most significant dimensions to this was the beginnings of economic redemption. Put simply, those first Christians discovered a way of handling money together which effectively abolished need from among their number — Acts 2:44-45; 4:34. Just what the implications of this are for us we'll see later on. In the meantime, here are some

---

THINGS TO DO

Date done

1. Read Psa 145 back to God in prayer. ....
2. List twenty good gifts you have
   received from God. ....

3. Give thanks to Him for each one. ....

Lesson 2 THE RADICAL PRINCIPLE

One of the things we saw in the previous chapter is that God's heart remains generous towards us in spite of our sinfulness. In fact, the Fall has served to reveal even more of the Lord's love for His world. Read Rom 5:7-8, 15, 20. The more monstrous sin has become, the more triumphant is God's grace over it. However undeserving we are, He willingly and abundantly blesses us. It's His nature so to do.

We are mean by contrast. Such splendid generosity, such zeal to do good, is not characteristic of the human race. In this we do not reflect the glory of God.

Especially when it comes to material things, we have inherited our First Parent's coveteousness. We see wealth as something to acquire for our own benefit. We hang on to what we've got and only with reluctance give to the needy. Raising our own standard of living has become the major preoccupation of the Western world.

This is not to say that people don't give. There are plenty of successful charities to prove otherwise. And even those who invest money in hope of a profitable return may also genuinely wish to create jobs and to produce something useful for society. But the root problem remains: since the Fall man has become a 'getter'.

Something radical needs to take place in the human heart, some change of outlook which will restore to us the loving heart of God. Just what that means is the theme of this chapter.

15

The effect of the Gospel

Jesus changes lives from the inside and it's that which leads to a change in the way we live. Read Eze 36:26-27. What four things does God say He will do for us?

....

....

What does He say He will remove? ....

What will be the effect? ....
Read also Heb 10:16.

Colossians 3:10 tells us that we have put on a 'new self'.
What is happening to it?

....

One of the most important signs that we are becoming like God is that we begin to love as He does. See 1 Jn 4:7-12.

The love of God isn't just words or a feeling. It's always 'love in action'. Read 1 Jn 3:16-18. In your own words, what loving action do you think John is commending?

....

The effect of the Gospel is to change us from being 'getters' into becoming 'givers'. Having been born of the Spirit, we now have the nature of God within us. So, we start becoming like God in the way that we live.

This means we can approach the issue of our money and possessions from a totally new perspective.

New resources, new purpose
One of the key passages in the Bible which reflects this radical change of heart in the material realm is 2 Cor 9:8. The RSV renders it best: 'God is able to provide you with every blessing in abundance, so that you may always have enough of everything and may provide in abundance for every good work'. To make sure you have grasped it, answer these questions:

1. What is the source of the believer's wealth? ....

2. What can we expect for ourselves? ....

3. Where is the abundance to go? ....

It's a very different way of looking at things, isn't it? The unbeliever looks to himself for his wealth. He wants as much as possible for his own comfort. He gives away very little, if anything at all.

The renewed Christian, by contrast, looks to God for an abundant supply. He only requires 'enough' for his own needs. (We'll see how to assess that in the last chapter). He wants as much as possible to go towards the blessing of others.

The following diagram illustrates the difference:

UNBELIEVER
Covetous

BELIEVER
Generous

Thinks he gets
from world
around him

Receives
from God
with thanks

Gives a
tiny amount
to charity

Gives to
bless every
good work

Spends on
enhancing lifestyle

Enjoys enough
for own needs

That's how it should look. However, there are many Christians who don't live like this. This may be because of either an attitude of covetousness or an attitude of poverty.

The spirit of covetousness

Every believer is created by God to be by nature a giver. Unfortunately, not all realize this. Many people become 'believers' without becoming true disciples. This, sadly, is often due to a faulty preaching of the Gospel which demands only mental and emotional assent without true repentance. Read Lk 14:28-33.

What do we have to count? ....

What do we have to give up in order to be a true disciple of Jesus?

....

Jesus demands a radical change of lifestyle for all who follow Him, especially in their attitude towards wealth. Look up these references — Mt 6:19-21; 19:21-4; Lk 9:25; 12:21, 33: 15:13; 18:24-25; 19:8-9.

Jesus knows that it takes drastic measures to break the spirit of covetousness. Our failure to be so thorough has left many Christians living like this:

BORN AGAIN
Unrepented covetousness

Gets from world
around but
honours God
with lips

Coins in
the plate

Better lifestyle than
ever because of
'fringe benefits' of
Gospel

('Fringe benefits' include giving up expensive habits such as smoking, excessive drinking and gambling; being able to borrow tools, cars or holiday homes; sharing meals or baby clothes; obtaining free professional advice, and getting jobs done cheaply or for free. These are all good things but are not the solution to coveteousness; they may, in fact, increase it.)

The spirit of poverty

The other problem which besets many believers in the realm of finance is a poverty spirit.

Many people in our society have a low sense of self-esteem. This often reveals itself in a passive attitude towards life. Apathy, indifference, low expectations and limited resources are all characteristics associated with it.

People with such an outlook may not necessarily be truly poor, but feel and act as if they are. There is little evidence of faith for joyful abundance in their lives. They begrudge spending money unless it's essential. They tend to 'make do' and this may well show in the way they provide for their dependents. When they give, it's more out of a sense of duty than real pleasure. Things are always 'tight'.

They look something like this:

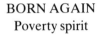

BORN AGAIN
Poverty spirit

Works hard
to make ends meet

Gives but
without real faith
or joy

Reluctantly
spends on
household needs

There are many scriptures which encourage us to have a different outlook. We'll be considering some of these later on. Meanwhile, look up these promises of our Lord Jesus — Mt 6:33; Mk 10:29-30; Lk 6:38; 11:9-10.

Both the covetous spirit and the poverty spirit rob us of our inheritance in Christ. They lock us up in the prevailing secular ways of thinking. In the next chapter we'll consider some steps which will set us free.

THINGS TO DO

Date done

1. Write down six examples of covetousness which you see in the world around you. ....

2. Write down any deed of 'love in action' which you have performed this past week, and any done towards you. ....

3. Discuss with someone you know whether you tend towards either a covetous spirit or a poverty spirit — or even both at once! ....

Lesson 3 CHANGING YOUR OUTLOOK

The covetous spirit and the poverty spirit are actually quite closely related. Both are never satisfied. The covetous man wants more — and usually gets what he wants. The man with the poverty spirit wishes he had more but never seems to get it. Both are thoroughly locked into unbelief.

In this chapter we're going to consider five steps of repentance and faith which will liberate our spirits from 'the deceitfulness of wealth' (Mk 4:19) and bring us into the financial will of God.

1. Correct your view of reality
Modern man is a materialist. He has no place for the truly supernatural or the living God. What we experience through our senses is all there is. Hence, the only things worth living for are material. Get what you can while you can. Eat drink and be merry, for tomorrow we die — and that's all there is to it!

As Christians we see things completely differently. Our eyes have been opened! Although we by no means despise the material world, we see it to be only a part of reality. There is a greater, spiritual realm. It's the world of 'the heavenly Jerusalem, the city of the living God. You have come to thousands upon thousands of angels in joyful assembly, to the church of the firstborn, whose names are written in heaven. You have come to God, the judge of all men, to the spirits of just men made perfect, to Jesus the mediator of a new covenant, and to the sprinkled blood' (Heb 12:22-24).

Our material world only exists because of the spiritual. Read Heb 1:3. How is the Universe sustained?

....

Do you think Paul is speaking only of Christians or of everybody in Acts 17:28?   (Underline)   Christians/Everyone.

There is nothing more important than our spiritual life. Living for this world only, investing all our energies in acquiring material possessions, putting our security in them, is blatant folly. That's why Jesus told the Parable of the Rich Fool — read it in Lk 12:13-21. Write out the last phrase of v.15 and try to memorize it. It's a very important truth.

'A man's life ....

....

How can we tell if we've got this right in our own lives? Jesus gives us a simple test. Read what it is in Mt 6:19-21. It's to do with where we put our savings! That's where our heart is, according to Jesus.

We all know how to invest on earth — banks, building societies, property and so on — but how do we invest in heaven? Eph 2:10 gives us a clue.

For what purpose have we been 'created in Christ Jesus'?

....

(N.B. We are not saved by works. Only the death of Jesus on our behalf is able to deal with our sins. But we are saved for works).

23

It's works of loving, merciful service which count before God once we're saved. These demonstrate that we consider heaven to be our most important bank.

Here are three examples of service:
> The service of worship — 1 Pet 2:5
> The service of caring — Mt 25:34-40
> The service of proclamation — 1 Cor 9:16-18.

If our real attention is given to serving the Lord, we'll maintain a correct view of reality and will have little heart for amassing personal fortunes.

Will you be the loser for this? Read Mt 6:33 to find out.

2. Cultivate a spirit of gratitude
Read Rom 1:18-23. What is the fundamental sin mentioned here?

(See v.21) ....

People who think they obtain everything by their own efforts or as their right have no cause to give thanks to anybody. It's only as we recognize God as the Source of all we have and are that we will be able to express our gratitude. Even then it's possible to forget. Read the warning in Deut 6:10-12. Which picture illustrates best your own attitude?

24

Write out Phil 4:6 and pray it into your life.

....

....

What is the will of God for us? — 1 Thess 5:16-18 ....

....

Giving thanks is more than saying grace before meals; it's a way of life. Practice doing so at every opportunity until you become a 'thank full' person.

3. *Identify with the poor*

Jesus began the Sermon on the Mount with these words: 'Blessed are the poor in spirit, for theirs is the kingdom of heaven' (Mt 5:3).

Being poor in spirit isn't the same as having a poverty spirit. Here is a list of some of the contrasts.

POOR IN SPIRIT	POVERTY SPIRIT
Recognizes need of God's grace	Feels needy and useless
Is open and vulnerable	Is independent
Is grateful to all	Feels deserves more
Trusts God to supply	Doubts if God really cares
Is content in all circumstances	Is usually discontented
Faithfully stewards resources	Buries talent in the ground
Shares blessings	Shares problems

Whether you have a wrong poverty spirit or are properly poor in spirit is not determined by how well off you are. It's to do with your relationship to God and His grace.

Once we've become poor in spirit we will find an affinity with needy people and want a practical involvement with them. For most of us the starting point will be with those in our own fellowship.

One of the glories of the true church is that all class distinctions are abolished — Gal 3:28. That has to be demonstrated practically. James has strong words for those who are choosy about the company they keep — Jas 2:1-9. Do you mix only with your own circle of friends in the church?

But love is giving, not just greeting. How are we to love?

See 1 Jn 3:16-18 ....

Loving care must extend to all whom God sends across our path. That's the point of the Parable of the Good Samaritan — Lk 10:25-27.

What is the mark of 'perfection' implied in Mt 5:46-48?

....

4. Become a faith giver
Write out Phil 4:19. It's a very important verse.

....

....

To understand the implication of this verse, imagine your material assets like a river.

The covetous man erects a dam and forms a lake. He may or may not acknowledge God as the source of supply, but certainly only a trickle reaches the needy. He is not in the flow of God's purpose in blessing him.

The man with the poverty spirit is little better off. All he finishes up with is a depressing swamp!

The 'faith giver', on the other hand, has learned how to tap into the Lord's abundant supply, and his streams spread outwards to bless many. He brings to pass the truth of Isa 41:17-20.

How do you become someone like this?

1. Tell the Lord this is what you want to be — an abundant receiver and an abundant giver.

2. Begin actually to give in the faith that the Lord will provide you with more to give. Read Lk 6:38. How will it be given to us?

....

....

That's how we're to give to others.

3. Renounce your hold on all your possessions. Every Christian has to do this in order to become a true follower — Lk 14:33. For some, though not all by any means, it requires that they sell all they possess. For example, the Rich Young Ruler needed to — Lk 18:18-25. From this passage, is it easy or difficult for the wealthy to be saved? (Underline) Easy/ Difficult. What do you think the wealthy must do?

....

1 Tim 6:17-19 gives some clear instructions to those who are well off.

You don't have to be comfortably off before you begin 'faith giving'. Whom did Jesus commend in Mk 12:41-44?

....

Why? ....

The poverty-stricken Macedonian Christians were actually able to give to the poor! Read 2 Cor 8:1-5 for their beautiful attitude.

5. *Examine your assets*
Giving includes sharing. What do you already possess? Do you have money locked up in investments just for a rainy day? Could this be released into the kingdom? Maybe you could buy property and rent

it out cheap to a young family, or make an interest-free loan to a newly-wed couple to enable them to buy a house.

Is your home cluttered with unused whims and fancies which could be better sold or given away so that others might benefit? Apply these tests to your possessions:

Do I use it enough to justify keeping it?

Do I really need it?

Is it worth the time and money I spend on it?

Would it be of more use to somebody else?

Remember, simplicity is a virtue. Keep your home virtuous!

Putting these five steps into action requires resolve and diligence but the blessings will be enormous. To help you on your way here are some more:

THINGS TO DO	
	Date done
1. Go and personally thank five people who especially bless you.	....
2. Write down ways in which you are involved with those more needy than yourself.	....
3. Go and speak with someone unknown to you next Sunday. Arrange to meet them socially.	....
4. Check that you've done the three points under section 4 of this chapter.	....
5. Make a list of some of your disposable assets.	....
6. Dispose of them!	
	....

Part Two MAKING MONEY

Lesson 4 FAMILY FORTUNES

The purpose of section one was to help us understand the radical change which must take place in our attitude towards money and possessions once we become Christians. Instead of looking upon the resources of this world as something to acquire for our own security, we are to view them as means of blessing others. If we do that, God Himself guarantees to provide enough for all our personal needs. In short, the key to financial freedom is to become a giver instead of a getter.

However, if we're to be givers, we must have something to give. We need resources.

This section is about those resources. In the three chapters we're going to cover:

● a new way of looking at the resources already at our disposal;

● the relationship between faith and God's abundance;

● a fresh motive for our daily work.

To tackle the first of these we must begin with the question

Who owns what?
Our concern in this study is with the management of our financial and other resources as individuals, rather than with economic

theories about whether the state or the private sector should hold the nation's wealth. In fact, it isn't really possible to argue the case for either capitalism or socialism from the Bible. We find both private and state ownership acknowledged in its pages. God's concern about justice transcends the limits of our current economic theories — but that's beyond the scope of this little book!

However, what we do have to consider when we discuss our individual finances is the question: just how 'individual' should we be about our possessions? After all, the moment a person becomes a Christian he ceases to live as an island; he becomes part of the family, a member of the body, a stone in the temple, a branch of the vine. He can no longer live 'privately'. Every aspect of his life, including his financial condition, is now affected by the fact that he has become part of the Christian community.

Just how radical the effect of the Gospel is on our attitude towards our material wealth can be seen in Acts 4:32. Write out this verse

....

....

....

What this is teaching is not communism but 'community-ism'. It is not a rejection of personal ownership, imposed by law, but a willing renunciation of what we might call 'mine-only-ship'. The discovery that they were brothers and sisters in Christ, and thus family, completely changed the attitudes of these early Christians towards their possessions. It released a spirit of sharing among them which touched all that they had. Instead of saying, 'It's mine' they now said, 'It's ours'. Possessions and incomes were from now on for the common good — see Acts 2:44.

What was the remarkable result of this sense of community wealth? Read Acts 4:34.

....

....

One big family
Community sharing on this scale doesn't come easy to us in our modern Western world. We are used to living by the dictum: what's mine is mine and what's yours is yours. And we install burglar alarms and mortice locks to make sure it stays that way! We are characterized by an individualism quite unknown in the ancient world.

Because we don't naturally think community-wise our minds need to undergo quite some renewing if we're to enter the practicalities of New Testament fellowship. We have to shake off the idea that the church is just an organization or a building and come to appreciate that it is a community of people living in fellowship as a family. It was this sense of becoming members of an enlarged family which led the early church to pool their resources as they did.

As we in our day rediscover the true nature of the church, we too will find that we're wanting to share our common resources more and more. We'll move away from an institutional view of the church's assets as just the buildings and monies held by the treasurer. Instead, we'll think increasingly of the church's wealth as the combined resources of all the members, for the common good. Truly a family fortune!

Recognizing our resources

There have been many different attempts by Christians at putting this into practice. Some have formed monasteries or communes, others have shared a common purse, a few have handed over the deeds of their houses to the church leaders. Most of these experiments have worked for only a few people in rather specialized circumstances. Some have run into real difficulties.

What we need are practical ideas for expressing 'community-ness' which almost any group of Christians can operate to advantage, without taking away the responsibility of each family to manage its own financial affairs, and without necessarily sharing a common purse under the same roof. Here are three pointers to help us think this through.

1. Have a willing attitude

It isn't possible to organize a spirit of sharing; this is something born in the hearts of those touched by God's love. Look up 1 Jn 3:16-18; 4:7-12. What do you think is the proof of God's love in our lives?

....

....

Nobody commanded the first Christians to pool their resources as they did. It was a spontaneous response to the glory of the Gospel in their lives. That this was no flash in the pan may be seen by looking at the same spirit in the Macedonian believers — 2 Cor 8:1-5. Family care-and-share was a hallmark of the early church.

Have you ceased to 'own' your possessions? Do you now find it a joy to share with your brothers and sisters what the Lord has blessed you with? Is there any area of reluctance about which the Lord is convicting you?

2. Make periodic assessments

Already quite a lot of sharing may take place in your fellowship on a casual basis and we are not suggesting for a moment that the whole thing should be systematized. But there is great value in occasionally taking stock of how we are doing in this area, if only that we might become more aware of our combined resources. There may also be needs which are being overlooked. This is especially likely if your church is growing fast.

Stocktaking exercises can be done at several levels:

a. We can sum up the total properties, goods, monies, skills and earning powers in our own household.

b. We can do this as housegroups. This is probably the most fruitful group to do it in.

c. We can assess our financial assets by congregations. Your church may, of course, consist of several congregations.

Here are some ideas as to how you can do this:

1. Assess what you have in terms of accommodation. The value of the property is unimportant unless you intend to sell it or use it in some other way to generate cash. Available space, e.g. a spare room, a large lounge or a garden is more important. Do you have access to a caravan or a country cottage? Does your home provide you with 'hospitality power'?

2. What investments or savings do you have between you? Are they necessary to live from or just sitting there for some vague future need?

3. What shareable items do you possess which might be useful to others e.g. washing machines, freezers, tools, cars, lawn-mowers, ladders, computers, camping gear, barbeques? You may well find that only one of a particular item is needed among several families.

4. Do you have unused items which could be sold, or given to somebody who could put them to good use? Remember, one person's junk is another's antique!

34

5. List how much money you earn between you. Don't be ashamed if you have a much better salary than others. God gave you that ability to earn. And if you are unwaged, remember that God has given you at the moment the tremendous gift of time. You have the power to provide thousands of pounds of labour at no expense to yourself!
6. Make a list of your combined skills. Do you have practical or artistic talents? Do you possess money-making gifts? Are you able to provide free services of some kind? Perhaps you have academic abilities which could help others.
7. Add up your total giving power as a group based on, say, your last year's giving.

Once you have done the exercise, you need to know what to do with these resources.

3. Put your wealth to work
Read the Parable of the Ten Minas in Lk 19:11-26. What was the sin of the wicked servant?

....

All that God has given us should be put to good use in His kingdom with a spirit of generosity.

1. Are there specific things the Lord has shown you that you should start sharing? Write them down.

....

....

....

2. Do you need to 'level things up' among you as a group? That doesn't mean all having the same. Needs differ widely, but nobody should be 'in need'. Read 2 Cor 8:13 to get the balance. Think creatively about how you can do this.
3. If your group is well-endowed you may be able to bless another group which is less well off in your congregation. Some sort of practical communication is needed among group leaders for this to work effectively. Could your administrator set up some suitable machinery?
4. Quite possibly as a whole congregation you'll be able to release resources into another poorer church elsewhere, either at home or abroad. Apostolic communication was the key to doing this in the early church.

Bringing an end to financial isolation is one of the finest testimonies we can have to the reality of our oneness in Christ. There's no more practical way of destroying selfishness and releasing the spirit of love among us. It's significant to note that in both Acts 2:42-45 and in Acts 4:32-35 Luke associates the believers' financial interdependence with a supernatural spreading of the Gospel. There are lessons here for all of us.

THINGS TO DO	
	Date done
1. Check that you've thoroughly repented of independence regarding your possessions.	....
2. Discuss the level of practical commitment which you have together as a housegroup.	....
3. In both your household and your housegroup do the exercise of assessing your joint resources.	....

Lesson 5 FAITH AND ABUNDANCE

There has been considerable debate over the issue of 'faith and prosperity' in recent years, to the extent that the words themselves have come to be identified with a particular school of thought on health and wealth. This is a pity because the words are biblical and belong to all believers whatever their particular views.

So-called prosperity teaching has brought some believers under condemnation for their supposed 'lack of faith'. It has left others wondering at the extravagant lifestyles of some of those who are 'believing the Lord'. Lots more just feel the whole thing is out of their reach.

In this chapter we want to arrive at a proper biblical understanding of what we can rightfully expect from our loving Father in heaven. In order to do so, we must clear up some misunderstandings.

1. Poverty is not necessarily the result of unbelief
We've already established the general truth that want exists as one of the bitter fruits of the Fall. But that doesn't mean the poorer you are the greater must be your sin!

To say of the individual that prosperity is a sign of the blessing of God and poverty a mark of his curse is too simplistic and runs contrary to the teaching of so much scripture. It is also patently false — there are multitudes of rich sinners in this world!

Poverty may exist for a number of reasons. Here are some given in the scriptures. Look up the text and write down the reason.

Prov 6:9-11 ....

Prov 11:24 ....

Prov 13:21 ....

Prov 13:23 ....

Prov 21:5 ....

Prov 22:16 ....

Prov 28:19 ....

Heb 11:36-38 (Note v.39!) ....

Nowhere did Paul accuse the poor famine-stricken saints in Jerusalem of either sin or lack of faith. He just took up an international collection for their relief!

2. The blessing of the Gospel is not primarily material
It's quite common in 'prosperity teaching' to compare Deut 28:1-8, 15-20 with Gal 3:10-4. Look these up for yourself. The question is put like this:

LAW = Blessing + Cursing
Jesus became cursed for us. Therefore
GRACE = Blessing

Hence, through faith only Deut 28:1-8 applies to us.

It looks attractive at first sight but it's not actually what Paul is saying. In fact, this approach misses the glory of what the scripture really teaches.

To understand the truth, we must recognize the difference between 'the curse of the law' and the curses contained within the law. 'The curse of the law' is explained in Gal 3:10-11. It means:

1. You are trapped in a system which requires perfect obedience.
2. You cannot be saved because salvation is by faith alone, but the law operates only by works.

So, even the 'blessings' of Deut 28 are part of the 'the curse of the law'. Living this way we are locked into a precarious system of blessing/cursing dependent on our obedience/disobedience to the Old Covenant legal system. It's like a pair of scales

Blessing   Cursing

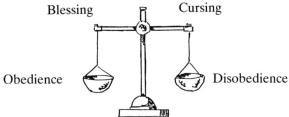

Obedience   Disobedience

Praise God, Jesus broke the scales! He redeemed us from the whole blessing/cursing system so that we could come into a different kind of blessing altogether. Let's remind ourselves of what this blessing is — read Gal 3:14. Write it down:

'so that by faith we might receive ....

This glorious promise of the Spirit liberates us from any sense of striving to get blessed by our own obedience. It also properly directs our hearts to our real inheritance, which is spiritual. Read 1 Pet 1:3-5. Where is our inheritance?

....

40

Through what are we shielded by God's power? ....

3. Faith is not a magic word
Faith is a word which gets bandied around. It's sometimes used merely to describe optimists or 'go-getters'. A 'faith person' may simply be aggressive, well-educated, confident, personable and an opportunist. People with different temperaments will just feel they lack 'faith'.

Equally, faith is often used these days to mean no more than speaking positively. The argument goes something like this:
> God is always sure that what He says will come to pass i.e. He has faith in His own words.
> If we 'have the faith of God' (literal Greek of Mk 11:22) we will, like God, be able to speak things into being, including our own material prosperity.

Now positive confession is all very fine and biblical (aside from this being a dubious interpretation of Mk 11) provided we are absolutely sure we are declaring the will of God. That requires both an accurate understanding of the scriptures and a revelation of the mind of the Lord in our present situation.

If we've already made up our minds that the will of God can only be our increased material comfort, we will only have 'faith' for that. But we can't for a moment say that our ease is always God's purpose; the Bible just doesn't teach that. Many believers have suffered unnecessary disillusionment because they have followed this sort of teaching. For the only logical conclusions for those who have things go wrong in spite of making all the right noises are either that they have a hidden 'lack of faith', or that God chooses not to hear them, or that the Word of God is false. Hardly a cause for encouragement!

41

Read Heb 11:1. The record of the true 'heroes of faith' which follows shows very mixed fortunes. In fact, not one of them received the promise in their lifetime. The reason for this is in v.40. What was it?

....

One other thing we must beware of is putting faith in 'faith' as a kind of catchword. 'I'm living by *faith.*' '*Faith* is what you need.' True faith is not a technique but a child-like trust in an all-loving heavenly Father, whatever the circumstances. Indeed, there will be many occasions when He deliberately allows us trying circumstances just to prove the reality of our faith. Here are just one or two of many references to look up — 2 Cor 1:8-9; Jas 1:2-3; 2:5. Read some of Paul's sufferings in 2 Cor 4:8-12. But how is he living — See 5:7? Write it down.

....

Does all this mean we should have no expectation of material blessings under the New Covenant? Are we to be worse off than some of the Old Testament believers? Do we have to spiritualize everything? I don't believe so. Provided we have undergone the fundamental change of heart which has freed us from covetousness and have surrendered our independence, we may enter many promises of abundance as God's people.

True prosperity
The key to understanding New Covenant prosperity lies in 2 Cor 9:11.

What does it promise us? ....

For what purpose? ....

The will of God is that we should prosper on behalf of others. The message is not 'give and you'll get rich' but 'give and you'll be provided with more to give in order to prosper others'. This 'give so that you can receive so that you can give' approach underlies Jesus' promise in Lk 6:38. How does He say God will give to us?

....

Returning to our basic text in 2 Cor 9:8 we find God wants to provide abundantly through us. God wants us to have faith to be prosperous givers. Exactly how we do this will occupy most of the third section of this book.

Prov 3:9-10 emphasizes this principle again. Keep in mind that the overflowing barns and brimming vats are given you so that you can generously share your wealth. The sin of the Rich Fool was not that he had so much, but that he held on to it — Lk 12:13-21. Sometimes God blesses us in advance just to see if we will share the blessing with others. It's a risky business not to do so!

Lk 12:21 speaks of being 'rich before God'. What does it mean? Consider the following illustrations and see if you get the point.

Investment in ourselves will not pass beyond the grave. It doesn't even bring real joy in this life — as many a rich person will testify.

Do we really believe this principle? Read Prov 11:24-26. What will happen to a generous man?

....

The Lord promises great blessings to his people as a result of the coming of the Messiah. Now that the Messiah has come we may claim these promises. Read, for example, Isa 60:5 and Jer 33:6-9. As a people we are heirs to divine resources. We should expect to have vast sums of money released to us for the work of the kingdom. There is every right to suppose that we can meet all the needs that God puts our way. Let's by all means have faith for that. And when it comes to passages like Deut 28 let's learn from them that when God blesses He really blesses. Without using any trite spiritual equations let's be stirred to great faith as we contemplate the incredible generosity of the Lord towards those He loves. His word is unchanging, 'I will bless you.'

Getting into the abundance
Read 2 Cor 9:6-7, 10. What do you think giving is likened to?

....

44

A friend once proudly showed me his pea plants. They stood in a neat row — all six of them, with nine pods on each. He had sowed sparingly, so that's how he reaped. I used to dig a shallow trench and throw in five hundred seeds. I got a big harvest.

This principle of generous seeding is true in all areas of spiritual life. If you want to be one who prospers the kingdom and has God himself guarantee to meet all your needs, you must 'plant' your money generously.

But this must be done in real faith, not under pressure. If money is the seed than faith is the soil. Rich soil will generate a hundredfold blessing; poor soil will yield a scanty return.

Many Christians give but seem unable either to increase their giving or to make ends meet. This is because 'the word has not been mixed with faith' (Heb 4:2). The reason for that may be because giving was seen only as a way of bettering their own lifestyle, or because of a temporary enthusiastic response, or because they were merely into some church 'commitment' to tithing.

What we suggest you do, if this is a problem, is to begin to give what you have real faith to give. And when you see that the Lord honours you, increase the amount by one per cent. Then repeat the exercise until God sets the ceiling.

Bringing in the Lord's dues is an act of faith and obedience. Most of us are in a position to at least honour Him with a significant percentage. If we do so, He promises to release great blessing into our midst. Read Mal 3:8-12. (Tithes here doesn't necessarily mean just 10%. Some have estimated that the Israelites gave more like 23⅓%.) We mustn't get under bondage to a percentage at this point. Just invest in faith what He has told us to in our own hearts. Write down the blessing He promises to bestow (v.10).

....

....

THINGS TO DO	
	Date done
1. Forgive any who you feel have put you under a wrong pressure to 'believe'.	....
2. Check before God that you really want a heavenly inheritance more than anything else.	....
3. If you need to, repent of criticizing God or His people for not apparently meeting your needs.	....
4. Ask for the faith to think big.	....
5. Start giving again if you've stopped.	....

Lesson 6 LABOUR OF LOVE

The single most important financial resource most of us have is our ability to work. This is the normal means through which God blesses us.

Miracles do occur, of course. Elijah got fed by ravens. Jesus fed the five thousand — and even on one occasion paid his taxes miraculously! — Mt 17:24-27. But the scriptures by and large put the emphasis on earning our living by the sweat of our brow. Even the mighty apostle Paul worked at tentmaking to provide for his needs when he felt the occasion demanded, which was a good deal of the time.

Work today is a vexed subject and it's beyond our scope to go into the matter too deeply. However, we do want to comment on three modern causes of discontent: job satisfaction, pay and productivity.

1. *Job satisfaction comes about by serving the Lord*
Nowhere does the Bible teach us that we have a right to a pleasant working environment, or a creative job with a fulfilling product at the end of it. In fact, the Fall means that a curse has fallen upon human labour. Look up Gen 3:17-19.

What is cursed? ....

What is required if we are to eat? ....

There is an element of futility in work — Eccl 2:17-26. Those at the bottom of the pile are often oppressed — Eccl 4:1. The Bible speaks strongly about this — see Amos 2:6-7; Jas 5:1-6. But in the end, even the rich have no satisfaction — Eccl 5:10-15. In spite of all the centuries, little has changed across the world. Man is no nearer happiness in his work.

But those who love the Lord, even if they be slaves, can enter into a remarkable relief from the curse. Read Eph 6:5-8 to find out how. What would you say the secret was?

....

What this actually means is that every Christian is in full-time service. Our daily work is no longer 'secular employment'. That means we can approach it with a sense of vitality and meaning.

2. *Serving the Lord has positive purpose*
Work serves at least three important purposes in our lives.

1. It allows us to demonstrate the kingdom to our fellow employees both by our conduct and our words. Read Phil 2:14-16. What is the secret of shining?

....

2. It acts as a discipline on our lives so that we do not fritter away the precious gift of time. Read 2 Thess 3:6-17. What happens if we're not busy — v.11?

....

48

3. It enables us to generate money for our own needs and the needs of those around us. Look again at 2 Thess 3.

Why should we work? — v.7-8 ....

....

What is the rule? — v.10 ....

....

Only where the church sees itself as a community of shared needs and blessings will this verse have any real meaning in the modern world.

Once we see our daily employment as a means of serving the kingdom it takes on a whole new sense of meaning. It's only when we look upon work as serving ourselves, our needs, our likes and dislikes, our comforts, that we run into trouble. Read Hag 1:3-11. What is the reason given for this sense of futility in their work?

....

This revolutionary sense of working to provide for the kingdom of God gives us every reason to want to be successful and to earn well. It sets us free from settling for mediocrity either in the way we work or over what we are paid. Many Christians need to get a better self-image about their worth to employers. We should actively seek promotions, both to obtain positions of influence for the Gospel and to earn the increased remuneration so that we can give more.

3. *Because we are serving the Lord we should be productive*
'A fair day's work for a fair day's pay, sufficient to keep an

employee and dependents in health, comfort and honour' is a good guide for both employers and employees. You might like to discuss the implications of this. But we may take it that a believer should render good service and do his job with a spirit of excellence. This should, at least, be marked by diligence, punctuality, honesty, friendliness and enthusiasm. What other characteristics would you add?

....

....

The Bible often rebukes laziness and describes it as a cause of poverty. Here are three examples — Prov 6:6-11; 21:25-26; 23:30-34. A slothful, undermotivated Christian cannot expect ever to generate abundant resources for the kingdom.

Previously dishonest people, thieves, fraudsters, shoplifters or tax fiddlers, should now live productive lives — Eph 4:28.

Why? ....

Housewives with a sense of community can gang together to develop home industries like the woman in Prov 31. She ran a clothing, a property and a retail trade from her home! It's time we broke the secular polarization of 'a career or a family'. Provided it is home based and causes no neglect to the family, there's no reason why housewives should not use their talents productively for the kingdom.

What about the unemployed? Our conviction is that no Christian of working age should be unemployed. You may be unwaged and drawing social security, but you shouldn't be idle.

Redundancy for the believer is an opportunity to serve in new ways. It is not an occasion for despair, even though the blow may fall hard and some really supportive counsel will be needed. 1 Thess 4:11-12 encourages us to make the best of the situation.

We've already intimated that the unwaged person can offer free service to the kingdom. It may be that the Lord is wanting you to start your own business, of course. There is much scope here. Has your church set up an advisory group to help in this?

If you are to start a Christian business, here are some pointers:

1. *Have a right motive.*
   If you want to get rich, you're on your own. If you want to give abundantly, the Lord will be with you.
   Set up a strategy for giving at the start of your business.

2. *Get the right business.*
   You need to take counsel in order to assess your own gifts, your potential product and your likely market.

3. *Employ the right principles.*
   Here are two dozen hints from the book of Proverbs on how to conduct your business.

   1. Honour the Lord — 3:9-10.
   2. Work with diligence — 6:6-11; 10:4.
   3. Seek divine wisdom — 8:10-11, 18-21; 16:16.
   4. Deal honestly — 11:1; 16:11; 20:23.
   5. Don't act as a guarantor — 11:15; 17:18; 22:26-27.
   6. Don't make money out of scarcity — 11:26.
   7. Go for realistic goals — 12:11; 28:19.
   8. Build the business steadily — 13:11.
   9. Develop a strong work force — 14:4.

10. Don't just talk about it; do it — 14:23.
11. Have nothing to do with backhanders — 15:27.
12. Take advice — 16:20.
13. Invest at the right time — 20:4.
14. Obtain security when dealing with dubious customers — 20:16.
15. Plan well ahead — 21:5.
16. Don't squander your assets — 21:17, 20.
17. Don't borrow too much — 22:7.
18. Deal only in righteous business — 22:16.
19. Don't run yourself into the ground — 23:4-5.
20. Organize your work — 24:27.
21. Employ only people you know — 26:10. (See also 2 Cor 6:14 about parternships with unbelievers).
22. Assess your business regularly — 27:23-27.
23. Don't rip people off — 28:8.
24. Make service, not wealth, your motive — 28:20.

4. *Treat your employees properly.*
Christian businesses shouldn't pay less than secular ones, nor provide poorer working conditions. If anything, they should provide better as a testimony to the joyful abundance of the kingdom. Read Eph 6:9; Col 4:1. Why should employers act in this manner?

....

Whether we are employed, an employer or self-employed, if we work in order to serve the kingdom of God we need have no anxiety about the future — Mt 6:24-32; Psa 37:16-22, 25-26. God will bless us so that we can bless. In the next section we'll look at how to distribute what He gives us. Meanwhile, here are some

THINGS TO DO

Date done

1. Write out a simple summary of your 'work worth' including skills, qualifications, work experience and vision. Are you in the right job? . . . .

2. Write down how you would assess your work if you were your boss. Do you deserve a promotion or a rise in pay? . . . .

3. Discuss the possibilities of starting 'home industries'. . . . .

4. Discuss what you can do for the unwaged. . . . .

Part Three   SHARING THE BLESSING

Lesson 7   GOOD HOUSEKEEPING

Money is like electricity: because of its great power it has to be handled properly.

Lack of proper channelling will cause electricity to drain away to earth. Too much poured into an unsuitable component will destroy it. Insufficient insulation will produce shocks. If switches aren't thrown, nothing happens.

In other words, electricity has to be organized. And so does money. In this chapter we're going to look at the proper management, or stewardship, of our personal finances. Husbands and wives should work this one out together. If you have older children, you may like to include them in the discussion for their own financial education. Single folk who share a flat will benefit from working through some parts together also.

Many Christians never become consistent givers simply because they are too disorganised over money. In fact, the opposite happens and they become debtors instead. In spite of this some still have a question.

A. Is it biblical to organize our finances?
. . . or should we live like the widow of Zarephath, who simply dipped her hand into the jar of flour every day and relied on the Lord to supply her needs? (1 Kings 17:7-16).   ·

Apart from occasional miraculous supplies, we generally find financial management commended in scripture. David had managers — 1 Chron 28:1. Jesus speaks of managers with approval — Lk 12:42; 16:2 (The original word here is the one from which we get 'economist' — a very different idea from the modern use of the term).

In Deut 14:22 the people are commanded to save ten per cent of their annual earnings for their pilgrimages-cum-holidays.

Taxes are to be allowed for and paid — Rom 13:6-7.

Money is to be systematically put by for the poor — 1 Cor 16:1-3.

The Bible commends commons sense in many passages. Look up these in respect of finance   Prov 13:16; 21:5; 27:23-4.

It is part of the husband's role as head of the household to take responsibility for the provision of his family — 1 Tim 5:8. However, the wife often has the most direct dealings with money. Certainly the shrewd wife of Prov 31:10-16 handled the extensive household accounts herself. This doesn't transgress the divine order, provided the husband doesn't abandon his responsibility to see that his family is provided for.

B. Organizing your accounts

Managing your money properly is really quite simple. All you have to do is think in terms of distributing your pay into a number of imaginary jam jars on the mantlepiece. You just keep a record of the number of spoonfuls you put into each and the number you take out. Naturally, you can't take out what you haven't first put in. So, unless you cheat, you'll never go into debt by overspending.

To operate this way you need either to open two bank accounts or to obtain two cheque books for one account. The first is the 'jam' account or cheque book; the second is the 'marmalade'. Use a bank which gives free services while you are in credit — which you always will be.

You'll also need a simple pocket calculator.

Your 'jam' account will actually hold the money which you place each pay day into several 'jam jars'. Your 'marmalade' account will handle your everyday spending.

First, you must set up the 'jam jars'. To do this you use a number of clearly marked accounts sheets, each one representing a jam jar. You'll need sheets with the following headings: Giving, tax (only if you are self-employed in Britain), bills, savings. To help you we've provided at the end of this chapter a sample accounts sheet which you may photocopy and enlarge if you wish. Take a look at it now.

The best time to start this is when you next get paid. Write down your pay and also all other available money you have — in your pocket, under the mattress, in any existing accounts. Make sure you know what your starting bank balances are.

All you do is divide your money up and write the figure in the IN column of each 'jam jar' sheet and in the BALANCE column. Do so on the following basis.

i. Total giving to God.

This should be decided upon in faith and in the light of the chapters which follow.

If you are a tax payer, all your giving (not just tithing) ought to be covenanted, preferably through your own church. A single signature made in good faith on a four year contract with your church (not the Inland Revenue) will allow the church to claim back all the tax you have paid on your giving. Normally, you can incorporate a release clause to cover an unexpected change in your fortunes such as illness, redundancy, pregnancy or moving away. Your church will, in any case, release you from your covenant under these circumstances. Ask the treasurer for details. It's very good stewardship to do this while we have the benefit of these tax concessions. (Self-employed people need to find out about deposited covenants from their treasurer).

Five reasons why you may not be covenanting:
a) You've never thought of it.
b) You don't understand it.
c) You're afraid you won't be able to keep up your giving.
d) You've been too lazy to do anything about it.
e) There's something wrong with your commitment to the church.

If you don't covenant, what is your reason for not doing so?

....

Do you need to talk about it with a friend/group leader/pastor/treasurer/accountant? (Underline which).

ii. Tax and welfare contributions.

These are normally deducted for you if you are an employed person in Great Britain, so you won't usually need this jar. If you are self-employed you should put money aside for tax purposes as you go. Don't wait until you get a bill from the tax man. Invest the money securely so that you earn interest on it. This money is not yours to spend or to borrow from!

iii. Bills

List all your major household bills such as gas, electricity, telephone, rates, water rates, insurances, mortgage/rent. Look back at previous ones and estimate the total amount you need to put by for one year. Add a percentage for inflation and divide this by twelve or fifty-two, depending upon whether you are paid monthly or weekly. This figure will be the money you need to put aside each time you are paid in order to save for these bills. However, until you have built up a decent balance in your 'bills' fund you will need to top it up with a bit more money during the expensive quarters.

iv. Savings

This may be money which you want to put by for your annual holiday or it may be for a large household item or a replacement car. See below about credit.

All this money needs to be put in your 'jam' account at the bank. You only ever use the 'jam' cheque book to draw from it. To ensure that you've got it right find out from the bank what your balance is. It should be the same as the total of all your 'jam jars' less any uncleared cheques.

What's left over from your money goes into the 'marmalade' account. This is for your ordinary living expenses and you write the balance on the cheque book stub or other record slip. If you are using two accounts you must make sure you credit that account with the same sum as you have written on the stub. Again check with the bank if you are not sure.

That's how you get started. Now, how do you spend money?

Very simply, each time you wish to pay, say, a bill, you make out a cheque for the sum from your 'jam' cheque book and you write the amount in the OUT column of the bills account sheet. You then subtract this figure from the balance (the reason for the calculator!) and write in the new balance in the third column. Here's an example of how the BILLS sheet might look after a while.

Date	BILLS	In	Out	Balance
1/1/86	Monthly sum put in	200		200
5/1/86	Rates		30	170
10/1/86	Insurance (House)		100	70
1/2/86	Monthly sum put in	200		270
5/2/86	Rates		30	240
24/2/86	Gas		130	110
28/2/86	Electricity		105	5
1/3/86	Monthly sum put in	200		205
15/3/86	Telephone		60	145

You may wish some of these bills to be paid by your bank by standing order. If so, make sure they come from your 'jam' account — and you must remember to deduct them from your balance on the BILLS sheet each time they fall due.

You could also, of course, have similar separate 'jars' for each individual bill if you want to be a bit more detailed. All you do is head up a sheet for each one and run it in the same manner as the others.

The 'marmalade' account is very easy to run. Every time you make out a cheque, whether for a purchase or for cash, you subtract the sum from your running balance on the cheque book stub. This way you'll always know what you've got left. Never spend it unless you've got it. If you use a cashpoint card you must also subtract the amount, even though you didn't make out a cheque.

The same goes for credit cards. Every time you use one, subtract the amount from your 'marmalade' balance. In effect, by doing this you are saving up for the bill when it comes in at the end of the month and this means you can simply make out a 'marmalade' cheque for the whole amount (only this time you don't need to deduct this from your balance, because you've already been doing that bit by bit) and pay it off without incurring any interest charges. See below on the use of credit cards.

C. The debt trap

Enormous numbers of people appear in our law courts because they are bad debtors. One of the major reasons for this is the vast 'credit industry' which has arisen in recent years. With every psychological trick in the book used to entice us into debt, borrowing money is easy; it's the paying back that's the problem.

Is it right for the Christian to run up credit? Rom 13:8 says literally, 'Owe no one anything.' It's interesting to note that the NIV has paraphrased this, presumably to accommodate modern borrowing practices, as 'Let no debt remain outstanding.' The debt may be acceptable provided you are keeping up with the repayments!

Of course, most of us enter some debt simply by obtaining gas and electricty on credit; and even the milkman delivers before receiving payment. But it's still possible to get behind even on these interest-free credit facilities. That's why you must put money aside to anticipate the bill — and pay it as soon as it comes.

But the real trap is the kind of credit which allows us to buy all manner of consumer articles at a high rate of interest. This may take the form of a hire purchase agreement or you may use a credit card. Both these forms of credit are bad stewardship because they are an expensive way of borrowing money.

Credit cards are especially suspect because they make the borrowing of money so simple and charge very high rates of interest on the outstanding balance. For this reason we strongly recommend that you operate by this principle: If you can't pay off the entire outstanding balance each month, assume that you are not gifted by God to use a credit card. Get rid of it.

Another version of borrowing is 'interest-free credit'. But actually the interest is built into a higher purchase price. Generally speaking, you should be able to buy cheaper for cash somewhere else. Mail order catalogues are particularly notorious for their high prices in this respect.

Most credit offers are based upon a coveteous appeal. Instant possessions, instant fulfilment. Write out the following caution once more.

Lk 12:15 ....

....

You may, of course, already be struggling with debt. How do you get out of it? Here are some simple steps:

    i. Face the facts. Get someone to help you do so.
    ii. Sort out your bills into an order of priority.
    iii. Decide what you can begin to pay off and write to each

creditor explaining how you intend to do so.

iv. Adopt the above budgeting system.

v. Destroy all your credit cards.

vi. Prune back hard on your lifestyle. Repent of covetousness.

vii Pray in the cash you need.

D. *Buy wise*

They say a fool and his money are soon parted. Make your expenditure a part of your prayer life. Is a particular item the will of God? Are you coveting or will it serve the Lord?

Plan your shopping. Make a list and keep to it. Avoid impulse buying. Remember that all advertising is designed to part you from your money. Buy in bulk where possible. As a housegroup you may be able to purchase from a cash and carry. 'Own brands' are usually cheaper and you can easily get used to the slightly different taste.

Consider your leisure expenditure. It's nice to eat out, but if you're going to be a real giver, you might find it better to share more home-cooked meals.

Do you need to keep up with the latest five-minute fashion or will it be sufficient for you to be more or less 'with it'? We're not suggesting you should be ten years out of date! Buy good quality clothes as a basic wardrobe and learn how to change your style creatively with some well-chosen but economical accessories.

Do you really need the central heating up that high?

How much do you spend upon records and tapes which soon go out of date?

Use the phone off-peak. Don't use it for long conversations when you could pay a personal visit.

Do you set fire to money by smoking?

Don't use the car for short journeys. You'll be fitter and wealthier if you walk.

Do you live on expensive and unhealthy convenience foods or have you learned to cook? A bit of skill with cheaper foods will usually improve your health, your palate and your waistline!

Buy season tickets and travel cards for journeys. Can you share a car to work with some friends?

These kinds of economies don't cramp your style. They actually improve the quality of life and at the same time save you money — that's a bargain! See how many more you can think up yourself.

E. Trust God

Wise management is good and proper, but we mustn't put our faith in it. Read Prov 3:21-6. Who is our confidence? When all is said and done, it is the Lord who supplies our needs and multiplies our resources. Good budgeting helps us make the most of these resources. The next three chapters show us the main reasons for doing so.

THINGS TO DO	
	Date done
1. Set aside two afternoons or evenings and reorganize your personal accounts, with the help of a friend if necessary.	....
2. Update your covenant giving by filling in a new form.	....
3. Review the amount of debt you carry. Can you reduce some of it more quickly?	....
4. Write down and implement ten practical ways you can live more simply.	....

Date		In		Out		Balance	

Lesson 8 SPREADING THE NEWS

We come now to consider the specifics of expressing God's love through our giving, and we begin with our concern for the spread of the Gospel.

The message of salvation does not come abstractly. Ever since 'the Word was made flesh' (Jn 1:14) the Gospel has been ministered through flesh, that is, through people called of God to fulfil this task. See Mt 28:18-20. Write down the kinds of ministry of the Word which our ascended Lord gave to us — Eph 4:11.

....

....

If we are to be realistic about spreading the Gospel we must provide financially for these ministries. It is a sad indictment on many churches that their leaders are some of the poorest paid people in society. Maybe that says what we really think of God's Word. It's little wonder that such churches see so little fruit. What is the reason given for the poverty of the people in Hag 1:5-11? (v.9).

....

....

65

We are profoundly convinced that the Gospel should be properly financed and that those who serve in this way should be adequately supported. The idea that poverty is good for humility is false and unbiblical. Even if it were true, we would hardly agree that the 'laity' don't need to be as humble as those who serve them!

Assuming we have God's heart and want to do the job properly, how should we proceed?

1. *The Old Testament pattern*
When the Israelites became a nation, God divided the land among the twelve tribes. However, He gave no inheritance of land to the tribe of Levi. These folk resided instead in forty-eight cities.and surrounding pasture lands which were set apart for their use.

The Levites were servants of the Tabernacle but were also dispersed throughout the land as upholders of the spiritual life and order of God's people. The sons of Aaron were the priestly family responsible for the sacrificial ministry in the Tabernacle. Their relationship to one another is given in Num 3:5-10.

Read Num 18:20-29 to find out how the Levites and Aaronites were supported. A tithe means 10%. So the Levites received 110% (11 tribes tithing to them) and they themselves tithed to the sons of Aaron.

During the restoration period under Nehemiah the people determined to obey God in this once more — Neh 10:37-39. Write out the last verse.

....

....

Commitment to the ministry of the Word in the Old Testament was spelt TITHING.

The blessing of God's people was directly related to their tithing. Their neglect of this in Malachi's day brought forth both a complaint and a promise from the Lord — Mal 3:8-12. The message is simple: feed my servants and I will feed you!

2. *The New Testament principles*
Who are the priests in the New Covenant? — 1 Pet 2:5,9

....

This priesthood is not an extension of the Levitical or Aaronic line. It has its source in Christ, and He comes from the line of Melchisedek — Heb 4:14; 6:20. There is then no Levitical or Aaronic priesthood to support under the New Covenant.

What we do find, however, are full-time servants of the Word of God — the Eph 4:11 ministries particularly — and the New Testament has clear teaching about their support. This consists of two complementary principles.

i. *Those who serve the Gospel have the right to our support.* Jesus taught this when he sent out the twelve and later the seventy-two — Lk 9:2-5; 10:4-8. In fact, whether the hearers did this or not was an issue of final judgement (10:12).

Paul taught the principle both generally and in the course of personal testimony. Read Gal 6:6; 1 Tim 5:17-18. 1 Cor 9:1-14 is noteworthy. Here he draws parallels with soldiering, farming and temple service to make his point.

Write out v.14...

....

John gives us an insight into the practice of hospitality and of sending on ministers of the Gospel properly supplied — 3 Jn 5-8. See also Rom 15:24.

The New Testament saints, like the Old, considered the ministry of the Word to be legitimate hard work worthy of financial reward.

ii. *Lack of finance should not be forced on the Lord's servants.* Whether to accept the support or not is a decision for the one ministering, not for the givers.

There are times when it is not expedient for a ministry to accept support. Paul felt this on numerous occasions and relied upon his tent-making skills to finance himself and his team — Acts 20:33-35; 28:30-31. What was his motive in this? — 2 Cor 12:14-16; 1 Thess 2:7-9; 2 Thess 3:7-10.

....

In 1 Cor 9:15-18 he presents another reason. What was it?

....

Nevertheless, he did accept support from some churches — 2 Cor 11:7-9 (N.B. 'robbed' is metaphorical!. The Philippian church was notably faithful in this — Phil 1:4-5; 4:10-20.

There were times of great hardship in the ministry — 1 Cor 4:11-12; 2 Cor 11:27. Paul's complaint to the Corinthians was that they seemed completely blind to this fact, even though they owed their very spiritual existence to him. He had never asked for their support, but they hadn't even offered!

Is your church and your heart like that of the Corinthians or the Philippians?

Write your answer here ....

Assuming we want to support the ministry of the Gospel, we must face the question.

3. *How much should we give?*
This is sometimes a vexed question but it needn't be. Even common sense tells us that God's servants shouldn't be paid any less than the average income of those they serve. But the issue isn't really, 'How much shall we pay him?' so much as, 'How much does he need in order to be set free from financial concerns so that he can concentrate upon the ministry God has given him?' Our privilege in giving is to release ministry, not employ someone to do a job for us.

In coming to this we must, of course, take into account the age, experience and family commitments of those who minister. There's quite a difference between the needs of a twenty-year-old single evangelist and a forty-year-old pastor with a wife and four children, for example.

So, factor one: Our giving must reflect the need which we are trying to meet.

It's not right to expect the Lord's servants to live according to our whims and fancies, let alone our moods and memories! You wouldn't want your employer to pay you like that, would you?

So, factor two: We need to give a realistic amount on a regular basis.

What does this mean? Should we do as they did in the Old Testament and tithe our income to the support of ministries of the Word? Here are some reasons in favour:

1. Paul draws a parallel in 1 Cor 9:13-14 between the support of the priesthood and that of the Word.

2. As the essential issue is the same i.e. people needing to be set free financially in order to fulfil a spiritual ministry, we should bow to divine wisdom and give ten percent. After all, it's the only clear specific figure which we are given in scripture for this purpose.

3. Abraham tithed to Christ via Melchisedek prior to the giving of the Law and we as his spiritual heirs should do likewise. (See below).

4. A tenth is a realistic figure for most people and makes at least a good starting point. After all, we presumably don't want to give less than they did under the Law for such a vital work.

5. There are many remarkable testimonies concerning the release of God's blessing on those who tithe. These suggest that promises such as Mal 3:10 continue to apply under the New Covenant.

A question is sometimes raised as to whether this isn't, in fact, a legalistic approach to the matter.

Assuming our concern is genuine and not just a cloak for reluctant giving, it's a valid question. After all, legalism is a major enemy of the Gospel. (If you give significantly less than ten percent to the support of ministry, you should make sure that your motives in raising the objection are pure ones).

If, on the other hand, you have a genuine desire not to be limited to ten percent . . . ! Our heart attitude should always be, 'How much can I give?' not, 'How little can I get away with?'

The answer is that tithing can be legalistic, but it doesn't have to be. None of the above points in favour of tithing is, of itself, a legalistic one. Legalism is a matter of attitude rather than actions, unless we can also show that the action was restricted to the dispensation of the Law and subsequently abolished in Christ e.g. blood sacrifices.

In fact, tithing did not originate with the Law of Moses. It preceded it and actually transcends it.

The first significant reference concerns Abraham and Melchisedek. Read Gen 14:18-20. This strange event is picked up in Heb 7:1-10 to demonstrate that the Levitical priesthood is subservient to Christ because Levi (yet unborn) tithed to Melchisedek through Abraham.

As Melchisedek is a model of Christ, in effect, Abraham tithed to Christ and with him the whole Mosaic system yet to be. A diagram may help!

LEVI & OTHER 11 TRIBES

71

Abraham is very important because he is the first truly New Testament man of faith in the Old Testament and, hence, a pattern for us to follow. Read Gal 3:29; 4:28. If he was able to tithe to Christ in a non-legalistic manner, leap-frogging the Law as it were, then we can do the same without fear of plunging ourselves into legalism.

The value of the Law is in giving us some guiding principle as to the use of those tithes i.e. to support full-time ministry — the point which Paul picks up in 1 Cor 9.

The joy of living under grace is that it allows us not only to tithe cheerfully but to go far beyond that if we wish, as we celebrate a better covenant.

4. *With what spirit shall we give?*
Everything under the New Covenant depends upon relationship. Salvation is less to do with what we know than Whom we know.

Write out Jn 17:3 ....

....

....

Tithing, or however much we give, must be done out of relationship. We give to the Lord. It's his ministry which we are supporting. We should do so with an attitude of love, trust and thanksgiving.

We believe the relationship issue should govern our giving to the human instruments of Christ's ministry. In the Old Testament they gave to the ministry which spiritually cared for them. Hence, the pastoral elders of our local church should be the prime recipients of our tithes.

Ten wage-earners (representing maybe fifty to eighty people — children, retired folk, students, unwaged housewives) can support one elder decently. A church where all the members do this can then maintain a healthy elder/people ratio by having several full-time elders. If money is given to the church treasurer he can ensure that an equable distribution is made. There may well be enough money coming in to support other, non-pastoral, ministries as well (evangelists, apostles, prophets etc.), especially if some folk start giving more than ten percent.

When you tithe (and logically this should be based on your gross pay before you purchase the services of government with your taxes) do so with love and prayer for the ministry which you are privileged to be able to support. Remember, you are releasing a ministry, not paying for services rendered — so don't give on the basis of how many pastoral visits you've had in the past month, or how good the sermon was! What attitude is commended in 2 Cor 9:7?

....

....

THINGS TO DO

Date done

1. List the ministries of the Word which you support. ....

2. Work out the percentage of your gross pay which you give to their support. Do you need to increase this? ....

3. If you give hardly at all to ministry choose a small percentage and begin to give as an adventure of faith. As God blesses you, increase the percentage until you reach at least ten percent. ....

Lesson 9 REMEMBER THE POOR

The second major area of giving which the Bible touches upon concerns our care for the needy. 'All they asked was that we should continue to remember the poor, the very thing I was eager to do' (Gal 2:10).

This is a very practical matter. The scriptures do not promise us a utopian dream for the solution of world poverty, let alone a political philosophy or economic theory. Jesus states categorically, 'The poor you will always have with you' (Mt 26:11). As long as human hearts are corrupted by sin, and while creation remains subject to futility, there will be poor people.

That doesn't mean we are to resign ourselves to greed and injustice or close our eyes to the poverty about us. The scriptures teach us to feed the hungry, clothe the naked, heal the sick, befriend the outcast and speak up for the oppressed. In fact, whether we do this or not is a test issue as to the reality of our eternal salvation. Read Mt 25:31-46. Who are we really serving when we bless the needy?

....See also Jas 1:27

1. *God cares about the poor*
Read Prov   14:31;   17:5;   19:17;   21:13;   22:9,16,22-23; 28:27; 29:7-13.

This concern of the Lord was expressed in the economic pattern which he established in Israel. He recognizes that our differing

75

physical, mental and creative abilities will lead to an inequality which, if allowed to grow unchecked, will result in injustice. Greed will cause the rich to get richer and fewer, while the poor will become poorer and multiply. This is known as emisseration. To prevent this happening, God instituted several checks and provisions. Here are some of them:

a) Sabbath year emancipation for all servants — Deut 15:12-18. This prevented 'class' from developing. How is the servant to be liberated? (v.14).

....

b) Jubilee restoration — Lev 25:8-17. All property was on a maximum fifty-year lease and the price was determined by how many years were left to run. What happened on the fiftieth year? (v.13).

....

This controlled greed and acquisitiveness.

c) Interest-free loans — Lev 25:35-38. This prevented people making money out of poverty. What happened to those who owed money after seven years debt? (Deut 15:1-5).

....

d) Specific provisions for the poor. What were these?

Lev 19:9-10 ....

Ex 23:10-11 ....

Deut 14:28-29 ....

e) The promise of miraculous provision — Lev 25:1-7,20-22. How were the Israelites to prove God in this?

....

We see God's care for the poor in the cry of the prophets. Read Prov 31:8-9. In these examples, what sins do you think they are lashing out against?

Isa 5:8..

Isa 58:6-10 ....

Amos 2:6-8 ....

Amos 4:1..

Amos 5:11-12 ....

2. *New birth, new impetus*
The coming of Christ was the fulfilment of many prophecies and the realization of many hopes. One of these was the sense of jubilee restoration. Read Lk 4:18-19. Write down five marks of this 'era of the Spirit'.

1. ....

2. ....

3. ....

4. ....

5. ....

This was amply demonstrated in the life and ministry of Jesus. Read Lk 7:22 for a brief summary.

The outpouring of the Spirit on the day of Pentecost led to a new sense of community care which dealt very quickly with the plight of the poor. Read again Acts 2:44-45; 4:32-35.

How important this was can be seen in the first act of church discipline — Acts 5:1-11. Why did Ananias and Sapphira die?

....

The first pastors (in my opinion) were appointed to care for the poor — Acts 6:1-6. In fact, that was where the Gospel flourished, as we note from Paul's observation in 1 Cor 1:26-28. Is your church bringing good news to the poor?

But their care was not restricted to their own. Read Gal 6:10.

Who are we to be kind to? ....

Who is our neighbour? See Lk 10:25-37 ....

By the time the church was three hundred years old it had the finest social services the world had ever seen, caring not only for its own poor but for all those around as well. You might like to discuss the question as to whether the church should ever have given this responsibility over to the state.

God's continued supernatural involvement with his people can be seen in his warning of coming famine — Acts 11:27-30. What was the immediate response of the saints?

....

This led to a major ministry of providing for the needy. Apostles began to take up collections for the poor. Write down how this was done practically. See 1 Cor 16:1-3.

....

Do you think we could do the same today? YES/NO/DON'T KNOW.

Do you have to be well off to give to the poor? See 2 Cor 8:1-5. YES/NO.

What is the highest motive for this sort of giving? See 2 Cor 8:9.

....

How will God provide for the poor through you? See 2 Cor 9:8-9.

....

Who especially should be generous to the poor? See 1 Tim 6:17-19.

....

What did Jesus command the Rich Young Ruler to do with his wealth? See Lk 18:22.

....

3. *Present practicalities*
Marxists claim that economic change will produce the new man and abolish poverty. Capitalists insist that given enough personal wealth we will then be able to give to the poor. The Gospel insists that only the new birth has the power to change our hearts sufficiently to make us love and care for the poor.

The church should be leading the way both in crying out for the needy and in providing abundantly for their want. How sad then that this is such a low priority in most of our thinking. The Old Testament people of God were specific and gave something like 3⅓% a year to the poor, in addition to the other provisions mentioned above.

Paul instructs us differently in 1 Cor 16:1-2. We should put some money by each pay day, according as God has blessed us. There is no particular percentage mentioned and giving of this kind is to be distinguished from tithing or other support of ministry, in any case. Some may be able to put aside only a very small percentage. Those better off may be able to give sixty or more percent to the poor. The determining factor is, 'How much have you been blessed by God?'

We have a call from God to deal with poverty. That involves imagination, faith and sacrifice.

IDEA!
God-given wisdom, e.g. 'Give a man a fish and he'll be fed for a day. Teach him to fish and you'll feed him for life.'

Believing God to supply abundantly and to do miracles.

Actually giving our money to benefit the poor.

We can begin by alleviating the poverty in our own churches. That may be done by direct giving of money or by the sharing of our resources as outlined in Lesson 4. Does your church have a 'fellowship fund' of some kind to provide a pool of finance for those needs which come to the attention of the elders?

You may not have a lot of ready cash but an open door of hospitality can be a tremendous encouragement to the poor — and don't forget, not all poverty is financial. What might just happen if you do this? See Heb 13:1-2.

....

We should then be looking further afield. Can our congregation bless another which is needier, say, in the inner city? What about being involved realistically with a church overseas, perhaps in a third-world country?

Write down who you think the poor are in this country.

....

....

Have you thought of helping the needy around you? You could start a 'Jesus Action' ministry of doing jobs for the elderly, the sick, those with large families and small incomes or single parent families. You may be able to help needy folk get their legal rights to welfare benefits. There's hospital visiting, taking elderly folk out, prison visiting, involving yourself with homeless people. Why not start some kind of unemployed club in which you also seek to help young people get jobs by training them in self-confidence, C.V.

presentation and job skills? You could try some job creation schemes, perhaps using government help. Write down a few ideas of your own.

....

....

....

Then what about involving yourself with constructive projects in a third or fourth world nation through an evangelical relief agency?

THINGS TO DO	
	Date done
1. Start regularly putting money aside for the poor on each pay day.	....
2. Write down and discuss the areas of need in your own fellowship and how you intend to meet them.	....
3. Discuss what help you could practically give to a poorer church.	....
4. Get involved in some kind of wider social ministry, maybe giving to overseas aid or a more local caring service.	....

Lesson 10 DESERVING CAUSES

So far we've concentrated on our giving to people — to those who minister the Word and to the poor. But there are other enterprises as well. These range from the purchase, maintenance and running of church buildings, through to starting Christian bookshops and other forms of Christian witness, to opening our own schools, hospitals and welfare services. These ventures require large sums of money.

Church buildings are notorious in this respect and some have questioned the whole notion of owning buildings, particularly as the early church appeared not to possess any. A few years ago, this led to some Christians abandoning such buildings in favour of meeting in homes. This was fine until those groups outgrew the available houses. From then on it became necessary to hire or purchase property.

Others have never left their church buildings but are often faced with high overheads as well as considerable renovation costs. On what grounds can we justify these expenses?

1. *The guiding factor*
What constitutes a deserving cause of this kind? The emphasis of the New Testament church is on the importance of people. The test of a venture then is, 'Does it serve the people?'

Church buildings mustn't become status symbols, religious museums or architectural flights of fancy. They are not to be temples. To model a church building in any sense upon the Old Covenant tabernacle or the temple is to betray a serious misunderstanding about the nature of the church. What is the true temple? Read 1 Pet 2:5-6.

....

This is not to say that a building should be merely utilitarian. The environment which we create says something about ourselves and our relationship to God — and that is surely much more than just a basic working one. We should express our love for God in artistic and conceptual terms wherever we can. What we must not do is to allow mere architectural extravagance at the expense of the needs of people — particularly if that means we have to ignore the needs of the poor in order to erect our monument. It's all a matter of finding the healthy balance.

We must remember too that our hope is not set upon buildings or any other project in this life. Indeed, there are times when we may be called upon to lose all these things. Read Heb 10:34. How did the saints accept this?

....

Why? See Heb 11:13-16

....

Provided we've got this right, we may believe God to enable us to spend large sums of money not only on church buildings but also on other people-serving enterprises. When we know we've got the principles right, let's do the thing with a spirit of excellence and generosity.

2. *The source of large finances*
a) The Lord is our great suplier. Large sums of money may cause us to quail but he is rich beyond all comparison — Psa 50:10-12. See again Phil 4:19. How will God supply our needs?

....

....

Our basic text in 2 Cor 9:8 promises an abundance for every good work. This is the realm for us to exercise our faith in the ability of the Lord to prosper the work of his kingdom. Let's never forget that many of the great church buildings and Christian institutions of the past were raised by men and women of faith who had to live far more precarious lives than we do today. We need to recapture the spirit of greatness in our hearts as we go for grand projects in Jesus' name.

b) Such ventures do require generous and sacrificial giving on our part. In the Old Testament two great schemes were undertaken — the Tabernacle and the Temple. Read how the people gave in Ex 35:4-9, 20-29.

Who was to bring an offering to the Lord? 'Everyone who was........

Who was to give labour to the Lord? 'Everyone who was...............

.... v.10

How often did the people give? Ch.36:3 ....

How much were they bringing? Ch.36:5 ....

Why did Moses have to stop them? Ch.36:6-7 ....

Do you get the impression that these people threw themselves totally and enthusiastically into the project? That's the only way to get something like this done.

Turn now to 1 Chron 29:1-20 concerning the Temple.

What did wealthy David give? v.2 ....

v.3 ....

How did the rest of the people give? v.6, 9 ....

Who did they recognize to be the source? v.16...........................

What was the result of their giving? v.20 ....

We need to capture the same generous spirit of these people. And they were doing this under the Old Covenant! When such occasions arise for us to give, let's do what these folk did and seek out all the hidden assets with which the Lord has blessed us so that we can prosper the work of God.

c) The wealth of the nations can be ours too — Isa 60:4-5. Some of this will be released as the Lord converts wealthy people but much more will come as we trade with the world.

Increasing numbers of believes are recognizing that God has

equipped them to make money for the kingdom by means of Christian business enterprises — as well as providing a testimony to godly business practice. It's beyond our scope to go into the ramifications of this, though we do commend the wisdom of Proverbs summed up in Lesson 6.

However, there are two points worth noting:

1. The elders of the local church are responsible for the lives of those in their care — Heb 13:7. That care extends to all areas of life, including business. But it doesn't mean the elders are either to initiate or run every deserving project, let alone the businesses which finance them.

At most, elders need only act in an advisory capacity when required. Businessmen need to get on with the job themselves.

2. When money is donated from a business to the work of the church, its distribution should be seen as an eldership responsibility. Read Acts 4:34-35. Who determined the distribution?

....

It's important not to give with 'sticky fingers'. Once money is given to the Lord, it's no longer ours to cling on to. Although consultation and discussion is appropriate, a giver should never seek to call the tune in a church by virtue of his wealth and influence.

Is your church thinking big? Are there projects you should be going for? Is any existing work suffering for lack of enthusiastic giving? Is your church treasurer always having to make appeals or does he have cause to cry 'Enough!'?

THINGS TO DO

Date done

1. Check the amount of money you give to the maintenance of your church building. Is it sufficient? . . . .

2. If your church is involved in a major project, ask God to release through you a sum of money you don't yet possess. . . . .

3. Discuss ways you could generate money for such projects. . . . .

Lesson 11 ENOUGH IS ENOUGH

Having spent the last three chapters on giving, and indeed having made that the fundamental thrust of the book, we come at last to consider what we should spend on ourselves.

1. *Finding the balance*

There are two extremes to avoid:
a) Spending too much.

We live in a materialistic society where most people believe, in flat contradiction to Jesus' teaching, that a man's life does consist in the abundance of his possessions. So we set out to acquire as much as possible, in the mistaken belief that this will provide us with security and satisfaction.

Christians are not immune to this temptation. Read Eph 5:5. What does Paul call the greedy person?

....

Self-indulgence is a false religion and no Christian can embrace it without committing spiritual adultery. We need to temper our spending in the light of this warning. Read 1 Tim 6:9-10. What is the root of all evil?

....

The Bible warns us of the deceitfulness of riches, that subtle ability of possessions to cloud our spiritual vision and to reduce our dependence upon God to a token. We must not allow ourselves too much. What choked the life out of the Word of God in Mt 13:22?

....

b) Spending too little.

Many Christians have reacted against materialism over the centuries by taking a path of self-denial. Some have gone into monasteries, others have become hermits, a few have deliberately inflicted pain on themselves. Much of this was based upon the belief that material things are inherently evil.

A less noble but related attitude can be seen today in those who begrudge spending any money on themselves and their dependents because anything that smacks of 'luxury', i.e. is non-essential, must be 'worldly'. This niggardly spirit often affects whole churches so that we find, for example, Christians 'making do' with tatty, down-at-heel, antiquated premises and facilities in the belief that it's not right to spend money on them – not exactly a demonstration to the world of the blessing of living under God's government! Worse is when this attitude is cloaked under a false ideological 'identification with the poor' which is far removed from the New Testament spirit.

Jesus was not an ascetic nor was He classed as one of the poor. Most of his life He worked as a self-employed craftsman and even during the three years of his ministry we never find Him having to beg. There is no virtue in poverty.

God promises to prosper the righteous – Prov 3:9-10; 10:22; 11:25. Although our contention is that a righteous man is one who is always abundantly blessing others, nonetheless, God wants that man to enjoy plenty of blessings as well. Those who honour the Lord financially will have no lack of good things. Note the context as you write out the last phrase of 1 Tim 6:17.

'God, who ....

Frugality isn't faith. Brother Andrew, in his book *God's Smuggler,* recounts the story of how he used to resharpen his old razor blades when he was living by faith until one day he realised that he was, in fact, living by unbelief in treating a new blade as a luxury.

Faith does not mean dowdiness or asceticism. It's all too easy to mistake the poverty spirit to which we referred earlier for sacrificial faith. Low expectation, always making do, forever patching up, may look at first sight like good stewardship but can be often no more than a misplaced set of values.

For instance, how much valuable time is consumed trying to repair the unrepairable when it might have been better simply to have trusted God for the money to replace the item? (That's not to say we must simply conform to the throwaway consumer society. It is often genuinely worth repairing things and many of us have saved thousands of pounds by doing so).

We are not to be stingy people. What's it like eating at the table of a stingy man? Prov 23:6-8.

....

Generosity is a hallmark of Christianity. It's particularly important that our children, while being taught the value of things, do not suffer from having mean parents. It is a good idea for groups of parents to discuss this issue so that they come to a fairly mutual idea as to what constitutes enough for their children. This can save a lot of envy, competitiveness and resentment among them.

Reaping follows sowing. That's a fundamental law of life. This means we do have to invest and spend money. We should always seek to do so in faith that the Lord will provide for us. Don't be afraid to spend out. Sometimes folk from very poor backgrounds feel a sense of guilt at doing so. Provided you have sought the Lord over it there is no need for this.

What we are looking for is a holy sense of proportion, a balance. Read Prov 30:8-9. What did Agur ask for?

....

What was he afraid of? ....

2. *Differing gifts and needs.*

People are not equal either in their abilities or their requirements. We start life with varying fortunes, some rich, some poor. Our temperaments, intelligences and dexterities vary. We may or may not have had all the opportunities we deserved – possibly because of injustice against our parents, our race or our sex. We may or may not have taken all the opportunities we were given — perhaps because we were too idle, apathetic or short-sighted.

But whatever our initial lot in life, it is a fact that generally speaking the wisdom for living which comes from obeying God's Word will substantially improve our material state. For example, Prov 3:1-2; 16:20; 13:21. Becoming a Christian changes our values for the better and this has a beneficial effect on our lifestyle.

However, there are still many factors which may cause our needs to vary from those of others:

i. Living in a cool climate means we have to spend more money on food, clothing, heating and housing than those who live in warmer climes.

ii. Wealth itself is relative to a very significant degree. We may earn a lot compared with people in other parts of the world but then it costs that much more to purchase the necessities of life. (This is not to overlook the fact that our real income is still much higher than that of the poor. Our idea of 'enough' must be tempered by their poverty).

iii. Where we live in our own country affects our requirements. God may have called you to live in an inner city situation or, equally, in a quite affluent part of the country.

iv. Then there's the size of your family, the age of your children, the kind of job you do.

More subtle are the psychological needs peculiar to you. Some folk feel they must have a garden, others couldn't stand the idea. A musician may want a piano, a handyman a workshop, a gregarious person a large lounge, and so on. Our hobbies and interests have a bearing on our needs.

Write down any other factors which you can think of.

....

....

All this tells us that there are no simplistic answers to the question of how much is enough. We cannot make either a list of rules, or even less, a list of approved possessions. It's really a matter of having a sensitive spirit before God. To help us in this here are

3. *Some simple tests to apply*

These are directed at our hearts rather than our heads; they serve as indicators of our souls rather than rigid rules. It may help if we draw a parallel between the amount of possessions we have and the amount of food we eat. Very simply, the person who becomes fat, spotty and slothful is overeating and needs to go on a diet. If we find the equivalent happening to us over our possessions, we need to adjust our lifestyle.

So, you have too much:

1. When possessions become a burden, demanding to be served rather than serving.

2. When things distract you and make you grow spiritually dull, e.g. the television damaging your prayer life or your fellowship with people.

3. When you are becoming significantly better off than others in your church and your giving is not increasing proportionately.

4. When your contentment is coming to depend on what you have amassed around you.

5. When you find, in practice, that you have forgotten the poor.

6. When you purchase things without the peace of God or the ability to give unqualified thanks.

7. When you are becoming anxious about your possessions.

8. When pride, arrogance and 'distancing' enter your heart.

9. When your home has become cluttered with virtually unused whims and fancies. Some people are like squirrels hoarding their nuts for winter!

THINGS TO DO	
	Date done
1. Write down any areas where you consider you spend wastefully or excessively.	....
2. Write down any area where God is convicting you that you've been too frugal.	....
3. Discuss how to get a right set of values across to children, especially in the light of advertising pressures.	....
4. Take time to assess your own lifestyle in the light of the above tests.	....
5. Implement whatever adjustments God tells you to make.	....

THE LAST WORD

The theme of this study book has been the handling of our money in accordance with God's will. Far from money being a distasteful necessity, having little to do with our spiritual lives, we've seen that it can be a great blessing. In fact, how we manage our finances is a fair barometer to the state of our Christian lives.

In the face of global economic inequality and financial insecurity, God calls us to a simple faith in his abundant provision and a love which will cheerfully share the blessing with those around us. It may not seem wise in the world's eyes, but behind it is the power and wisdom of God. Every one of us can enter into the economic provisions of the kingdom of God and bear testimony to his faithfulness.

All it requires is that we don't pick and choose from the truth. We must embrace the whole package, otherwise we won't get it right. Having completed the course, it would be a good idea to review your progress. The simplest way is to read the contents page and then go over all the 'Things to do' in order to make sure you've done them.

God wants to bless you and to make you a blessing in the way you handle your money and possessions. He desires His Word to prosper in your heart and bring prosperity to many through you. And above all other gifts He wants us to remember Jesus and continually to cry with the apostle Paul, 'Thanks be to God for his indescribable gift!'